Spot the Difference
Christmas

by Genie Espinosa

ARCTURUS

ARCTURUS

This edition published in 2019 by Arcturus Publishing Limited
26/27 Bickels Yard, 151–153 Bermondsey Street,
London SE1 3HA

Copyright © Arcturus Holdings Limited

Illustrated by Genie Espinosa
Written by Lisa Regan
Designed by Trudi Webb
Edited by Sebastian Rydberg

ISBN: 978-1-78950-255-8
CH006952NT
Supplier 29, Date 0619 Print run 8264

Printed in China

Can you find
me on every page
of the book?

JINGLE BELLS

Jingle all the way into Christmas by spotting ten differences between these two pictures.

HE'S MAKING HIS LIST

You'd better not be on the naughty list!
Spot ten differences here.

FIRST TO BE FESTIVE

Are your decorations up yet? Bet you can't beat this!
Find ten differences.

DEAR SANTA

Take time out to find ten differences
in this festive scene.

BUSY BUSY

Not long to go, but plenty of work to be done!
Find ten differences in this hectic workshop.

HOLLY AND IVY

These two festive fairies are here to help you be good!
Find ten differences.

A HELPING HAND

Kitty loves decorating the tree! Can you see ten things that have changed?

ALL ABOARD

See if you can spot ten differences before the
Christmas Express leaves the station.

FUR-LEGGED FRIENDS

Have fun spotting ten differences while
Santa takes care of his beloved helpers.

SPECIAL DELIVERY

Christmas is a time for visiting friends.
See if you can spot ten differences here.

SILENT NIGHT

Shh! Enjoy the peace, and spot ten
tiny changes in the second scene.

HOWLY NIGHT!

The silence is shattered! Plug your
ears and look for ten differences.

A CHRISTMAS COTTAGE

Yummy! Can you spot ten
tasty differences?

TASTY TREATS

Christmas baking is the BEST!
Which ten things are different here?

A SNOWY SCENE

Santa is all shook up! See if you can spot
ten differences through the snow.

ALL TOGETHER

Some jobs are easier with lots of help!
Find ten differences here.

DECK THE HALLS

Teddy loves Christmas, too!
Where are the ten differences here?

WINTER WONDERLAND

Look for ten differences in this
cuter-than-cute Christmas scene.

IN THE BLEAK MIDWINTER

Prepare for a long winter with these hibernating animals, and find ten differences.

THE BIG SWITCH-ON

Ready . . . steady . . . lights!
Find ten differences to illuminate your day.

WHITE CHRISTMAS

It should be easy to spot ten
differences in this white-out!

IT'S A WRAP

Presents! How exciting! See if you can
spot ten sneaky differences.

PILE THEM HIGH

Even more presents! And ten
more differences to find . . .

IT'S SNOWTIME!

Let's head outdoors to spot ten more differences
in the crisp, fresh air.

CROWD PLEASER

Can you spot ten differences in
the busy Christmas market?

FUN AT THE FAIR

There's so much to do at this Christmas fair!
Keep an eye out for ten differences.

IN A SPIN

Join in the fun by spotting ten differences between these scenes.

TWELVE DAYS OF CHRISTMAS

Twelve differences for twelve days.
Can you spot them all?

ON THE SLOPES

Wheeeee! Spot ten differences before the snow melts!

ELVES ON SHELVES

The elves are decorating the house.
Have you spotted all the differences?

CHRISTMAS KISSES

Love is in the air at this special time!
Look for ten differences.

A STAR IS BORN

Shine your light on ten differences
between these little performers!

GOOD KING WENCESLAS

Look out on this snowy land
to find ten differences.

OPEN UP

What do you think is behind each window?
Can you find ten differences?

SO SUITE

The Nutcracker is an exciting Christmas tale.
See if you can spot ten differences here.

TIME FOR BED

It's Christmas Eve—but who can sleep?
Find ten differences, and then close your eyes.

READY FOR TAKEOFF

Look carefully for ten last-minute differences
before Santa takes to the skies.

Some creatures are stirring on this Christmas Eve!
Can you spy ten differences?

LOOK UP!

Get set, Santa . . . go! Can you see him up above—
and spot ten differences?

A NORDIC NOËL

Look carefully for ten differences in this
super cool Christmas design.

CELEBRATE WITH A BANG

Whee! Find ten differences as you gaze at the celebrations in Moscow's Red Square.

"GOD JUL"*

*"Merry Christmas" in Swedish

Swedish celebrations start on St. Lucia's Day.
Can you spot ten differences here?

"FRÖHLICHE WEIHNACHTEN"*

74   *"Merry Christmas" in German

In Germany, Santa leaves good children's presents in shoes, while Ruprecht gives the naughty children a lump of coal!

Merry Christmas

"FELIZ NAVIDAD"*

*"Merry Christmas" in Spanish

Spanish celebrations continue into January!
Join the fun and look for ten differences.

DOWN UNDER

If you're lucky you might spot Santa being pulled
by kangaroos in Australia! Look for ten differences.

"GLEÐILEG JÓL"*

*"Merry Christmas" in Icelandic

Icelandic children receive presents from the Yule Lads, who might play tricks!

PIÑATA PARTY

In Mexico, children celebrate by breaking open a piñata known as a "posada." Enjoy finding the ten differences!

GRANDPA FROST

Russian presents are delivered by Ded Moroz and his granddaughter, Snow Maiden. Find ten differences!

A FESTIVE FEAST

The big day has arrived and it's time for food!
Feast your eyes and spot ten differences.

LET'S PLAY

After lunch it's time for a game.
Look for ten more differences here.

PARTY TIME

Make the most of the celebrations before party season ends!
Find ten festive differences.

HAPPY CHRISTMAS!

And finally . . . wishing you a happy Christmas from everyone!
(Oh—don't forget to find the last ten differences!)

ANSWERS

3 JINGLE BELLS

4-5 HE'S MAKING HIS LIST

6-7 FIRST TO BE FESTIVE

8-9 DEAR SANTA

10-11 BUSY BUSY

12-13 HOLLY AND IVY

14 A HELPING HAND

15 ALL ABOARD

16-17 FUR-LEGGED FRIENDS

18-19 SPECIAL DELIVERY

20-21 SILENT NIGHT

22-23 HOWLY NIGHT!

24-25 A CHRISTMAS COTTAGE

26 TASTY TREATS

27 A SNOWY SCENE

28-29 ALL TOGETHER

30-31 DECK THE HALLS

32-33 WINTER WONDERLAND

34-35 IN THE BLEAK MIDWINTER

36-37 THE BIG SWITCH-ON

38-39 WHITE CHRISTMAS

40-41 IT'S A WRAP

42 PILE THEM HIGH

43 IT'S SNOWTIME!

44-45 CROWD PLEASER

46-47 FUN AT THE FAIR

48-49 IN A SPIN

50-51 THE TWELVE DAYS OF CHRISTMAS

52-53 ON THE SLOPES

54 ELVES ON SHELVES

55 CHRISTMAS KISSES

56-57 A STAR IS BORN

58 GOOD KING WENCESLAS

59 OPEN UP